Mowgli is a human boy who was raised by a pack of wolves in the jungle. His best friend is Bagheera, a black panther.

A dangerous tiger called Shere Khan is looking for Mowgli. Bagheera decides to take him to the Man-village, where he will be safe.

When night falls, Mowgli and Bagheera find a tree to sleep in.

While Bagheera sleeps, a snake called Kaa hypnotises Mowgli. Bagheera wakes and knocks Kaa out of the tree, sending him slithering away.

The next morning, Mowgli is woken up by a loud noise. It's a herd of elephants!

Mowgli marches with the elephant patrol. "Hup, two, three, four!"

Then Mowgli meets a laid-back, fun-loving bear called Baloo.

Baloo teaches Mowgli all about the 'bare necessities of life'. Soon Mowgli can fight and scratch just like a bear!

Baloo promises the Man-cub that he can stay in the jungle with him for as long as he wants. Mowgli is very happy.

But suddenly, a group of monkeys swing down from the trees and kidnap Mowgli. They take him to their leader.

The leader of the monkeys is an orangutan called King Louie. He lives in an old temple.

King Louie promises to help Mowgli stay in the jungle if he will teach him how to make fire – but Mowgli doesn't know how!

Baloo and Bagheera finally find Mowgli in the monkeys' temple. Baloo dances with King Louie to distract him.

But as he tries to rescue Mowgli from the monkeys, Baloo knocks down an old pillar. The temple starts to collapse!

Bagheera picks Mowgli up and carries him away to safety.

Baloo decides
to help Bagheera
take Mowgli to
the Man-village,
but Mowgli still
doesn't want to go.
He storms away.

Baloo and Bagheera look for Mowgli. They know that Shere Khan is nearby and that the boy is in danger.

Mowgli is sad and lonely without his friends.

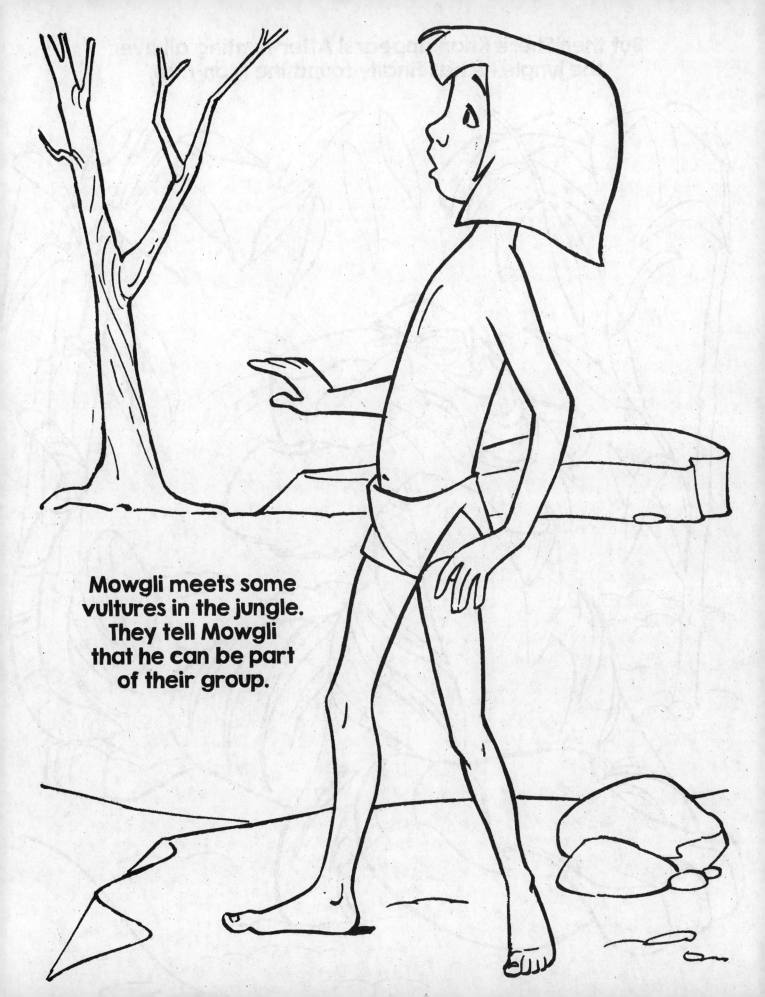

Mowgli meets some
vultures in the jungle.
They tell Mowgli
that he can be part
of their group.

But then Shere Khan appears! After hunting all over the jungle he has finally found the Man-cub.

But before Shere Khan can hurt Mowgli, Baloo arrives.
He tells Mowgli to run as fast as he can.

**Then Baloo grabs Shere Khan by the tail -
he won't let him hurt his Man-cub friend!**

**But before Shere Khan can hurt Mowgli, Baloo arrives.
He tells Mowgli to run as fast as he can.**

Then Baloo grabs Shere Khan by the tail -
he won't let him hurt his Man-cub friend!

Bagheera grabs Mowgli and takes him to safety before Shere Khan can escape.

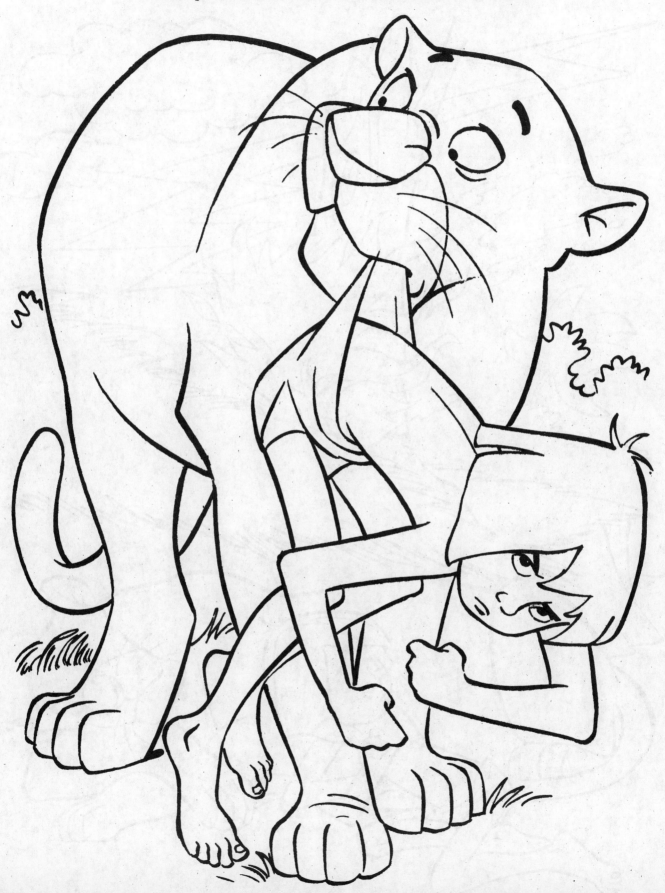

A storm breaks out and a bolt of lightning strikes an old tree, setting it on fire.

Mowgli knows that Shere Khan is afraid of fire. He grabs a burning branch from the tree and chases the tiger.

Shere Khan is scared and runs away into the jungle, never to be seen again.

**Shere Khan is gone forever.
They are all safe at last.**

Finally, Mowgli, Bagheera and Baloo reach the Man-village.

Mowgli notices a beautiful girl fetching water from the river. He has never seen another human before!

They go to the Man-village together, where Mowgli will be safe with his own kind.